ILLUSTRATED ANIMAL ADVENTURES

adapted by
GRAEME KENT

illustrated by
ERIC KINCAID

BRIMAX

INTRODUCTION

A man flees for his life through a jungle, chased by a huge dinosaur, and falls into a deadly trap prepared by a tribe of primitive hunters. A war-horse and his master charge into battle in the Crimea against terrible odds. The ugly runt of a litter of puppies shows great courage. A miner weighs down a jumping frog with lead shot in order to win a bet. An elephant, cast out by his herd, becomes a killer.

These are just some of the incidents and animals to be found in this book. The stories have been written by such famous writers as Jerome K. Jerome, Jack London, Mark Twain and Sir Arthur Conan Doyle.

These stories have been chosen for a number of different reasons. They are set in fascinating and unusual parts of the world—the frozen wastes of Alaska; the mining camps of the USA; the jungles of Africa; the remote moors of the West of England; a Russian battlefield.

The animals we meet and the men and women involved with them are so well-drawn that they almost leap off the page. A sledgedog risks his life to save his master; a highwayman's horse will let no one but her master ride her; a hunter grieves for the beast he has been forced to kill; a miner is unable to resist betting, and gathers all sorts of strange creatures about him.

Each tale has been written by a great story-teller, and this is obvious in the way that we are drawn along by the strength of the incidents described. Some of them are thrilling, others are humorous or fantastic. All of them deserve to be read again and again.

The stories in this collection have been selected and adapted by Graeme Kent, a primary school headmaster who has also been a producer of children's programmes for the BBC, and education consultant to six Third World nations. He is the author of over sixty books, published in a dozen different countries, and hundreds of television and radio scripts. His text-book series *Journey into Books* (Cassell) is used as an introduction to children's literature in many primary and middle schools.

CONTENTS

ISBN 0 86112 230 5
Published by BRIMAX BOOKS, CAMBRIDGE, ENGLAND.
Printed in Hong Kong

THE JUMPING FROG

by Mark Twain

Jim Smiley was a miner. In the winter of 1850 he was working in one of the great gold-mining camps of the American West.

Now Jim was a nice fellow, but he had one great weakness. He would bet money on anything. If he couldn't get anyone to bet against him on one side, then he would change over and bet on the other side. Any way that suited the other man would do for Jim. He was happy as long as he could bet. It did not matter what he was betting on.

If there was a horse-race, Jim would be there with his money. If there was a dog-fight, Jim would back one of the dogs. If there were two birds sitting on a tree branch, Jim would put money on which one would fly off first. If he saw a bug moving, he would bet cash on how long it would take to get where it was going. Then he would follow it to make sure.

Once, when the parson's wife was ill, Jim being a kind-hearted fellow, went to see her.

"How are you?" he asked.

"The doctor says I'm going to get better," the lady said.

Jim thought for a moment. "Bet you two dollars that you don't," he said in the end.

Jim bought a horse. It was old, slow and broken down. It was a sorry sight. At first the other miners in the camp used to laugh at it. If they held a horse-race they would give Jim's nag a long start. Naturally Jim would bet on it to win. When the race began Jim's horse would be nowhere at all for a long time. Then, in the last few seconds, Jim's mare would get all excited and come racing up to win by a short head.

Next Jim bought himself a dog. It was a bull-pup. Like the horse it was not much to look at. It was small and thin and sad. Jim used to match his pup in fights against all the other dogs in the camp. In contest after contest the bull-pup would be tossed at first, all over the place.

The other miners would bet against Jim's dog. When all the money was down Jim would give a shout. His dog would seem to go crazy. He would hurl himself on the other dog in a flurry of snaps and bites until his foe turned and fled.

One day, however, the bull-pup met his match. The bull-pup's pet move was to bite at his enemy's hind legs. Then a gang of miners put the dog up against a mut that had no hind legs. They had been cut off in an accident with a saw.

Jim's dog loafed around until all the money had been bet. Then Jim gave his usual shout. At once the pup went for the other dog's hind legs. Only there weren't any. First the bull-pup looked surprised. Then he looked fed up. He gave Jim a stare, as if to say that his heart was broken. That look seemed to be saying it was all Jim's fault for putting up a dog that had no hind legs to get hold of. The bull-pup gave up and limped off. He was no good as a fighting dog after that.

On the whole, though, Jim seemed to have a lot of luck with his animals. He had tom cats, and terriers and fighting cocks. He entered them in all sorts of events, and more often than not they won. The miners said that Jim was lucky.

Jim must have thought so as well. But one day he pushed his luck too far. He got himself a frog.

He caught this frog and said he would train it. He took the frog to his tent and spent three months teaching it to jump.

Jim spent all his spare time on this. By the time he had finished that frog could perform like a circus acrobat. It became a champion at catching flies. No matter how far away the fly might be the frog would leap through the air and swallow it.

Jim called his frog Daniel Webster. Jim knew that all he had to do was call out "Flies, Daniel, flies!" and the frog would take off into the air. Then it would flop back down on to the floor again.

But what the frog really became famous for was leaping across the ground. Miners would come from miles around to see it jump. They would bet Jim that the frog could not jump a certain distance. Jim would put up his money and then, as sure as fate, the frog would soar across the space.

Jim used to keep Daniel Webster in a box he had made. One day a stranger came to the camp. He saw Jim with the box, and said:

"What might it be that you've got in that box?"

"It might be a parrot, or it might be a canary," Jim said, "but it ain't – it's only just a frog."

The fellow looked in the box.

"Hmm, so it is," he said. "Well, what's he good for?"

"I'll tell you," said Jim. "He's good for one thing. He can out-jump any frog in this county."

The fellow took the box again, and had another long look, and gave it back to Jim.

"I don't see no points about that frog that's better than any other frog."

"Maybe you don't," Jim said. "Maybe you know about frogs and maybe you don't. Anyway, I've got my opinion. I'll bet forty dollars that he can jump farther than any other frog in the county."

The man thought for a moment, and then said sadly, "Well, I'm only a stranger here, and I ain't got no frog; but if I had a frog I'd bet you."

At once Jim said, "That's all right. If you'll hold my box a minute, I'll go and get you a frog."

The man took the box, and put his forty dollars down next to Jim's, and sat down to wait.

He waited on his own for some time, and then he had an idea. He reached into his pocket and took out a handful of small metal pellets used for shooting ducks.

Then he took Jim's frog out of the box. He opened its mouth. Carefully he poured the shot into the frog, filling him almost up to his chin.

Jim was still out in the swamp looking for another frog. He had to slop around in the mud for a long time, but finally he found one and took it in and gave it to the man.

"Now, if you're ready," he said, "put your frog next to Daniel Webster. I'll give you the word to start."

The two men put the frogs on the ground, side by side.

"One-two-three-jump!" said Jim.

Both men touched their frogs from behind. The new frog hopped off. Daniel Webster, weighed down by all the shot that had been shovelled into him, gave a heave, but he could not move. He was planted as solid as an anvil.

Jim was surprised and disgusted, but of course he had no idea what was the matter with Daniel. The other fellow took the money. As he was going out of the door he jerked his thumb at Daniel Webster, and said:

"Well, I still don't see no points about that frog that's better than any other frog."

For a long time Jim stood scratching his head and looking down at Daniel Webster. The frog did not move.

"I do wonder why that frog didn't jump," said Jim. "I wonder if there ain't something wrong with him. He looks mighty baggy, somehow."

As he spoke he lifted Daniel Webster up.

"Why, blame my cats," he said. "He must weigh five pounds."

He turned the frog upside down. All the pellets of shot poured out of Daniel Webster's mouth. Jim was the maddest of men. He put the frog down and chased out after the other fellow, but he never caught him.

FOR THE LOVE OF A MAN

from "The Call of the Wild" – by Jack London

Buck was a sledge dog. Some said that he was the best in all the cold lands of the North, where men looked for gold.

It was his job to lead the other dogs who pulled the sledge of his master, John Thornton. Buck was given this job because he was braver and stronger than the rest.

Buck was a wild dog. He sat by John's fire at night, but he could still hear the call of the wild things from the great dark forest. When he fought he fought like a wild beast, with teeth and claws. He fought to the death. Kill, or be killed, it was the only law he knew.

He had won his place as the leader of the nine-dog team in a fierce fight. The chief dog before him had been Spitz, a strong white husky. As soon as Buck had joined the team Spitz had started to steal his food and to drive him away from the fire at night.

Buck had put up with this for a short time. Then he knew that he would have to fight Spitz, or starve to death.

The battle took place one evening on the hard-packed snow. As usual Spitz tried to drive Buck away from his food.

Buck did not cry out. He drove at Spitz, shoulder to shoulder. Both dogs rolled in the snow, Spitz on top. Twice his teeth clipped together, like the steel jaws of a trap. Buck pushed himself to his feet. In vain he tried to sink his teeth into the neck of the big white dog.

Time after time Buck rushed at his enemy. Spitz kept driving him back. Soon Buck was soaked in his own blood. He knew that he would not last much longer.

Now the other dogs were sure that Spitz would win. But Buck had one trick left. Again he rushed at Spitz, as if to hit him with his shoulder once more. At the last second he dived low, just above the snow. His teeth closed on the other dog's left front leg.

There was the crunch of a breaking bone, and the white dog faced Buck on three legs. Still Spitz fought on, but there was no hope for him. In another minute or so he lay dead on the snow. The team had a new lead dog.

There was only one living thing that Buck loved, and that was his master John. For months of each year John lived in a tent pitched on the snow between a forest of pine trees and a great frozen river. When the snow stopped falling and the wind dropped he would go out on his sledge, pulled by Buck and the other dogs. For day after day they would travel over the ice and snow while John looked for gold.

Buck adored his master. John looked after his dogs. After a day's work he would feed them with dried fish and then talk to them for hours. He would pat them and play with them.

Buck used to lie at his master's feet, looking up at his face as John spoke. When John moved about the camp, Buck would follow him, keeping close to the miner.

Twice in a short time Buck was able to save his master.

No other man meant anything to Buck. The other miners saw this one day in Clay City. John had made the long journey there to buy food.

After he had put his food away in his sledge, John went to the saloon for a drink. He took Buck with him. The dog lay on the floor, his chin on his paws. He did not take his eyes off his master.

It was then that 'Black' Burton, the bully of the city, came in. He was a big man with a quick temper.

Soon Burton started to pick a fight with a small man who stood at the bar. John tried to stop the bully. Burton hit him as hard as he could.

John was sent spinning. He held on to the bar to stop himself
falling. Burton came towards him, his fist held high.

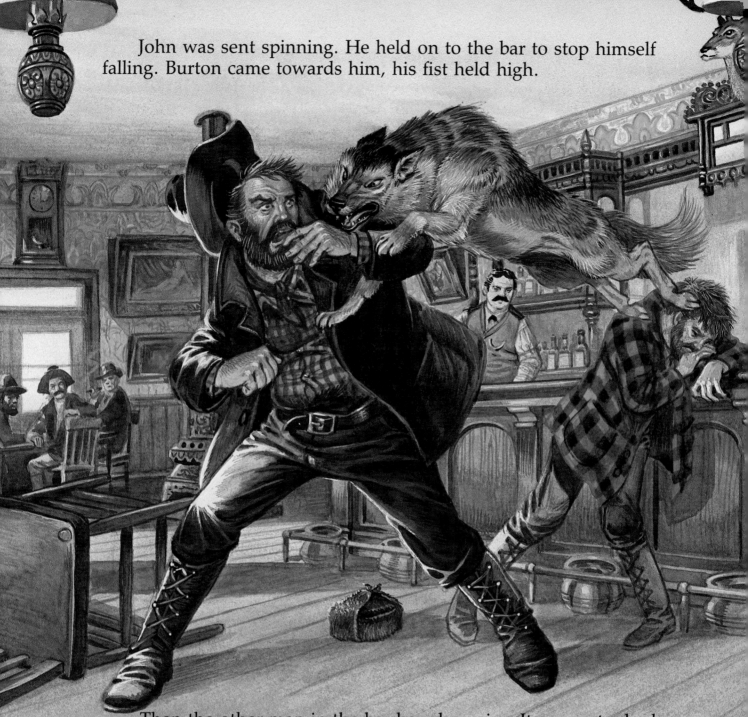

Then the other men in the bar heard a noise. It was not a bark,
nor was it a yelp. It was more of a roar. They saw Buck's body rise
up in the air as he left the floor. The dog sprang at Burton's throat.
    The big man saved his life by putting up his arm. Then he fell
to the floor, with the dog on top of him.
    Buck took his teeth out of the bully's arm and went for his
throat again. This time his teeth sank deep into Burton's neck.
    The other miners managed to drive Buck off, but still he stood
by the door, barking until he was sure that his master was safe.
    The miners held a special meeting to make up their minds what
to do about Buck. In the end, they said that the dog had done the
right thing in helping his master. Burton should not have hit John
in the saloon.

Not long after that Buck saved his master again. Summer had come. The ice on the river had melted. John was taking a boat down the river with two friends, Hans and Pete.

The river was wild and fast-moving. John was in the boat, using a long pole to move it through the water. Hans and Pete were on the bank, holding on to a long rope tied to the craft, in order to keep it steady. Buck was standing with them. As usual his eyes were on John.

The boat was getting near a very rough patch of water. There were many rocks poking out of the white foam. The boat began to be carried along quickly.

The two men on the bank did not know what to do. Hans wound his end of the rope round a tree. This made the craft come to a sudden halt. It turned right over and sent John flying into the water.

The helpless miner was in a wild stretch of the river in which not even a swimmer could live. Buck sprang into the water and swam straight towards his master. He fought his way through the foam until he reached John's side.

The miner reached out and held on to the dog's tail. Buck turned and tried to drag the man back to the shore.

He could not do it. The force of the rushing water was too strong. John and Buck found that they were being dragged down the river towards a number of great sharp rocks sticking out of the water like black teeth.

John knew that he could not reach the river bank. He scraped over one rock, crashed into a second and then held on to a third. He let go of the dog's tail.

"Go, Buck, go!" he shouted.

Buck was swept on down-stream. He heard his master's shout and raised his head out of the water. He could see the shore and he could hear Hans and Pete calling him.

Without the weight of his master clinging to his tail the dog was able to swim back towards the river bank. It was hard work, but in the end he got close to land. Hans and Pete were able to drag him on to the bank.

Both men knew that John would not be able to hold on to the rock for long. As fast as they could they tied one end of a piece of rope about Buck's body, holding on to the other end.

"Go back to John," cried Pete. "Swim, Buck, swim!"

Again the dog pushed out into the wild foam. This time he was swept past his master and on down the river by the power of the water.

On the bank Hans and Pete pulled on the rope and dragged Buck back to the land. The dog had hurt his ribs against a rock and had swallowed much water. The two men pumped the water out of him and Buck jumped back into the river.

This time he heard his master call out faintly above the roar of the water. He knew that John must be very weak.

Buck swam with all his might, taking the rope with him. This time he held on until he was in a straight line above John. Then he turned and let the force of the water sweep him down-river.

He went through the hissing foam with the speed of a train. He hit John with great force. The man let go of the rock and clung to Buck and the rope.

On the shore Hans and Pete started to tug on their end of the rope. Buck and John were pulled under the water and dragged towards the shore. Dog and man crashed against rocks and scraped along the bottom of the river, holding on to each other. After what seemed an age they reached the bank and were dragged on to dry land.

When John came round he stood up and limped over to Buck. The dog was lying on the ground, his eyes shut. Gently John felt him all over. He found three broken ribs.

"Right," said John. "We camp here."

And camp they did, until Buck's ribs healed and he was able to travel again.

A ROUGH RIDE

from "Lorna Doone" – by R.D. Blackmore

When I was about fifteen, I was big and strong for my age. Working all hours on our Exmoor farm in the West of England had made me that way. I also thought too much of myself. However, a meeting with a horse was to bring me down to earth in more ways than one.

One dark and wet November evening, my younger sister Annie and I went out into the farmyard to see what was making our ducks so noisy.

It had been pouring down with rain for a week past. The river which flowed close to our house had risen over its banks and was in full flood.

The ducks were scattered all along the rushing water's edge. They were staring out at the swollen water and quacking like mad things.

There in the middle of the water was a tree. Caught up against this tree was a gate which had been torn from its hinges and carried away. Clinging to the top of this gate and in danger at any moment of being swept off and drowned was our old drake, the father of most of the ducks on the farm.

Annie screamed at the sight of our beloved old bird in such danger. I liked not the look of it but I began to wade into the fierce current.

A man on the back of a horse came suddenly round the corner of the great ash-hedge on the other side of the stream.

"Ho, there!" he cried, "get thee back boy. The flood will carry thee down like a straw. I will do it for thee."

With that he spoke softly to his mare. She was young and proud and the colour of a strawberry. She arched up her neck, as if disliking the job but trusting her rider.

With dainty steps she entered the water. The rider gripped her sides with his knees, urging her on. She stopped and looked back, wondering. Then she went on until the water rushed over her shoulders.

The mare tossed up her lip, as if scorning the danger. Then the rush of the water swept her away and down the stream, past the gate. As they struggled through the water the man leaned forward in his saddle. He plucked the drake from the gate and carried him away.

In a moment all three were carried down-stream. The rider, still holding on to the drake, lay flat in his saddle and made for a bend of smooth water.

They landed some way away in our kitchen garden, where the winter cabbage was. Annie and I crept through the hedge to thank the rescuers. The man would not answer us until he had spoken to his mount.

"Sweetheart," he said gently, "I know you could have jumped across, but I had a good reason for making you swim. Well done, my Winnie."

Some way from us the drake clapped his wings, shook the water from his body and waddled off to his admiring family. The rider dismounted and looked at us.

He was short but strongly-built, fresh and ruddy-looking, with a short nose and keen blue eyes. He had a merry way with him. Yet he had a sharp, stern air, like the crack of a pistol if he did not like something.

"Well, young 'uns, what are you gaping at?" he asked.

"Your mare, sir," I said bravely. "I never saw such a horse. Will you let me ride her?"

"You could never ride her, lad. Winnie will carry no one but me. She would throw you off and kill you."

"Ride her?" I said with scorn. "I can ride any horse on Exmoor. Only I never use a saddle. Take it off."

The man looked at me and grinned. "The ground is soft enough for you to fall on," he said after a while. "Come out of this garden though, for the sake of the cabbages. By the way, I am your mother's cousin. Tom Faggus is my name, as everybody knows. And this is my young mare, Winnie."

What a fool I had been not to have known at once! Tom Faggus was the great highwayman. He was the most famous robber in these parts, and was famed for many daring hold-ups and escapes.

His mare Winnie was almost as well-known as her master. I had been a fool to offer to ride her, but I could not back down now for the sake of my pride.

Mr Faggus gave his mare a wink and she walked after him until we reached the open field.

"Are you sure, boy?" he asked me.

"Can she jump, sir?" I asked. "There is a good take-off on this side of the stream."

Mr Faggus laughed quietly. "A good fall-off, you mean. Well, there can be no great harm in it for you. We are a family of thick skulls."

"Let me get up," I said angrily.

Tom Faggus looked hard at me. Then he began to remove the saddle. Men from the farm were beginning to run up to see what was going on.

Tom spoke softly to the mare. "Not too hard, my dear," he told her. "Let him down gently into the wind and mud. That will be enough."

He took off the saddle. I leapt on to Winnie's back. I pushed the mare into a walk and then a trot. She moved easily, as if pleased to find such a light weight upon her back. In my ignorance I thought she knew that I could ride a little, and was afraid of me.

"Gee-up," I cried, showing off in front of the others. "Show what you are made of," and I dug my heels into her sides.

Tom Faggus whistled. The horse took off like a great spring uncoiled. I felt her hind legs coming up under her and I knew that I was in for it.

First she reared upright in the air. In doing so she struck me full on the nose with her neck, bringing my blood flowing. Then she stuck her fore feet in the mud and kicked her hind ones to the heavens. Finding me still sticking to her like wax, away she flew with me.

I was being carried faster than I had ever ridden before. Winnie drove straight at a stone wall.

"Jump off, John!" screamed my sister.

At the last moment the mare turned with the speed of light. We were so close to the wall that my knee brushed against it.

"Mux me!" I cried, for my breeches were broken, and short words went the furthest, "if you kill me, you shall die with me!"

Then Winnie took the courtyard gate at a leap, knocking my words between my teeth. She went over a hedge and headed for the water-meadows. I lay on her neck and wished I had never been born.

We seemed to be faster than the wind and to scatter the clouds as we went. All I knew of the speed we made was the flash of the mare's shoulders, and her mane like trees in a tempest. I felt the earth under us rushing away, and the air left far behind us. My breath came and went. I prayed to God, and was sorry to be so late doing so.

All the long swift while I clung to Winnie's shoulders. I dug in my finger-nails and toes. I was proud of holding on so long, though sure of being beaten.

In a fury at feeling me on her still, she jumped across the wide water-trough sideways, to and fro, until no breath was left in me.

Branches from the trees whipped across my face, and thorns from the bushes scratched my hands and arms. I longed to give up and die quietly on the ground.

Suddenly there came a shrill whistle from close to the house. The mare stopped, as if shot. Then she set off for home with the speed of a swallow, and going as smoothly and silently. I had never dreamt of such gentle movement.

I sat up again, but my strength was all spent, and no time left to recover it. At last, as the mare rose at our gate like a bird, I fell off into the mud.

"Well done, lad," said Mr Faggus, as they all gathered round me. "Not at all bad work, my boy. I did not think you would stick on so long."

"I should have stuck on much longer sir, if her sides had not been wet. She was so slippery."

"Boy, you are right. She has given many the slip," said the highwayman with a laugh. "Vex not because I laugh, John. Winnie is like a sweetheart to me, and better than any of them be. None but I can ride my Winnie mare."

ELEPHANT HUNT

from "Trader Horn" – by Trader Horn

The elephant is a mighty beast. As a rule he does harm to no one. But from time to time one is driven away from the herd by the others. This rogue elephant may then become a danger to all men. I was to find this out for myself.

I had been a trader on the Ivory Coast of Africa for many years, but the beauty of the land always amazed me.

On this trip I had been visiting the villages along the banks of a great lake. I sailed my large canoe from place to place. It was piled high with such trade goods as bags of salt, knives, plates, files, guns and gunpowder. These I would exchange for carved canoe paddles, elephant tusks and any other goods the people had to offer.

The water of the lake around the canoe was as clear as dew. I spent hours staring over the side at all the wonders beneath the surface. I marvelled at the fish, the coloured rocks, and the weeds that waved in the water and shone as if the sun was pouring colour into them.

After a number of days I left the lake. The twenty men I had hired paddled our canoe up a wide and winding river.

On either side great trees grew down to the water's edge. Gay parrots, butterflies and dragon-flies swooped in and out of the trees and skimmed across the water in front of us. As we passed the sandbanks lining the shore huge crocodiles slipped into the water and eased their lazy way across the river. Tick-birds perched on the heads of these great creatures and picked their teeth free from insects. Hippos wallowed in the mud on either side of our craft.

That night we slept on a sandbank. I always chose such a place to rest because cool breezes would blow over them. But the night was not a quiet one. For hour after hour I could hear animals coming down to the water to drink. I could hear the growl of the tree-leopards, the chatter of monkeys, and from time to time the unusual sound of the great gorillas beating their chests with their fists as if they were drums.

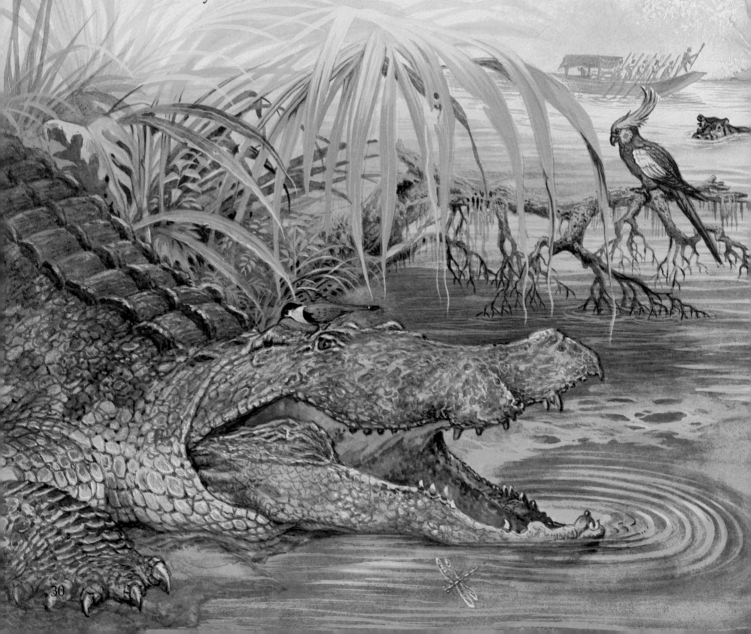

Early the next morning we set out again. Ahead of us lay an island in the middle of the river. White-winged sea-birds who had made the long journey inland from the Atlantic to lay their eggs, fluttered about us as we paddled.

Waiting just off the shore of the island was a large war canoe. A dozen warriors came out in the canoe to greet us. Seated in the prow was an old chief I knew well. He hardly spared the time to greet me before he was talking quickly.

"Ojuga has struck again, trader," he said urgently. "He has killed two children from my village. He cannot be far away. You have the most powerful rifle in this part of the country. Will you go after him? You are our best chance."

I nodded. Ojuga was a great killer elephant, famed throughout the area. Years ago he had been cast out of his herd because he was so fierce and bad-tempered. He had become a lonely night prowler. Over the years he had killed many men and women from local villages. The name Ojuga meant Hunger.

"I'll do my best," I told the chief. "Which way did he go?"

The old man pointed up-river. "That way," he said. "He left the village about an hour ago. Take care, trader."

31

For several hours my helpers paddled the canoe past the trees crowding down to the river bank. I held on to my Snyder rifle. I had three of them in the canoe. The other men had their spears, the long sharp weapons known as *assegais*.

After a time we turned into a narrow stream leading off the main river. We slowed down and looked from side to side. We seemed to sense that the beast we were hunting was not far away. We rounded a bend and saw something that made me tighten my hold on my rifle.

On the left-hand side of the stream, walking slowly along the bank, was a huge bull elephant. He was the biggest of his sort I had ever seen. His skin hung loose about his sides and legs, looking like mud-coloured overalls. His great nodding head held two large tusks jutting out ahead of him.

He entered the water some way in front of us. Filling his trunk with water he sprayed it all over himself. We had a fine view of him.

I could have shot him and perhaps killed him while he was crossing the river, but the great beast always held his head in such a way as to make it hard to shoot him through the eye, one certain way of killing him.

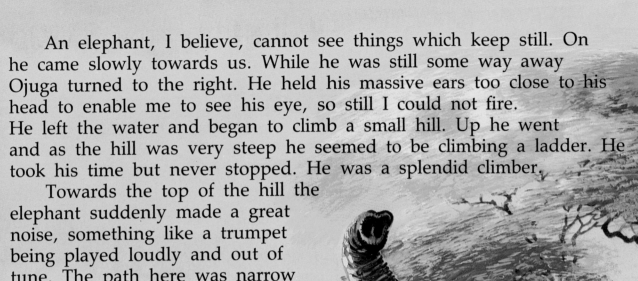

An elephant, I believe, cannot see things which keep still. On he came slowly towards us. While he was still some way away Ojuga turned to the right. He held his massive ears too close to his head to enable me to see his eye, so still I could not fire. He left the water and began to climb a small hill. Up he went and as the hill was very steep he seemed to be climbing a ladder. He took his time but never stopped. He was a splendid climber.

Towards the top of the hill the elephant suddenly made a great noise, something like a trumpet being played loudly and out of tune. The path here was narrow and the great beast wanted to make sure that he had a clear path ahead.

Then, for no apparent reason, Ojuga stopped and half-turned. This was my chance. I fired. No result. I fired again, with a rifle handed to me by one of the men in the canoe. Another shot behind the ear, no result. The elephant began to lumber away.

I jumped out of the canoe on to a sandbank and aimed my rifle again. Before I could press the trigger the great beast suddenly fell backwards. The shots had taken effect.

Ojuga was almost at the top of the hill when he fell. He seemed to bring most of the hill down with him. Down, down he came, amid a shower of loosened rock and a cloud of dust. He fell into the stream, just ahead of the canoe, with his head on the sandbank and his huge body in the water.

I ran along the sandbank. The elephant was quite dead. The hind part of his body was covered with a pile of rock and dust.

I sent two of my men to fetch the chief. He must have been following close behind, because it was not long before the war canoes came into view.

The old man stepped out on to the sandbank. He shook my hand and thanked me.

"You were lucky, trader," he added.

"How so?" I asked.

"I have known Ojuga since I was a boy," the old chief said slowly. "He was hunted by my father and my grandfather before him. Once, when I was a young man, I even managed to throw a spear into his side, but he went away and healed himself. One day he returned and charged at me while I was picking bananas. Two of my men shot him at close range, but Ojuga turned and trampled them to death. He has lived long and done much harm. But now he lies here, the greatest of all elephants."

Fires were lit and the men and women danced. They made up a new song. I am told that it is still sung to this day. The song went: "Ojuga was mighty and feared. He slew many men, but now he is slain and eaten."

As the dancing and singing went on through the night, I found that I was becoming sad. I thought about the beast I had shot. He had been a noble sight in his life.

I wondered what Ojuga could have thought about being cast out of his tribe and forced to wander by himself for year after year. He must have had a lonely time of it.

Perhaps in a way I had helped him by shooting him on that hill. He had been growing old. Sooner or later he would have gone down to drink in the swamp and would have found that he could not pull his great weight out of it.

The death that I had given him had been grander than that. There had been majesty in his great fall from the hill.

MONTMORENCY

by Jerome K. Jerome

There were four of us – George, and William Samuel Harris, and myself, and Montmorency the dog. We decided that we should have fresh air, exercise and quiet by taking a boat up the river Thames.

Everyone was keen on the idea, except Montmorency. He never did care for the river, did Montmorency.

"It's all very well for you fellows," he seemed to complain, "you like it, but *I* don't. There's nothing for me to do. Scenery is not in my line, and I don't smoke. If I see a rat, you won't stop; and if I go to sleep, you start fooling about with the boat, and slop me overboard. If you ask me, I call the whole thing stupid."

We were three to one, however, and the matter was agreed. We decided that we would sleep out on fine nights and hotel it, and inn it and pub it when it was wet, or we felt like a change.

Montmorency was greatly in favour of this. He likes company. Give him something noisy and not very nice and he is happy. To look at Montmorency you would imagine that he was an angel sent upon the earth, for some reason unknown to mankind, in the shape of a small fox-terrier. There is a sort of Oh-what-a-wicked-world-this-is-and-how-I-wish-I-could-do-something-to-make-it-better-and-nobler expression about Montmorency that has been known to bring tears to the eyes of old ladies and gentlemen.

When he first came to live with me, I never thought I should be able to get him to stop long. I used to sit down and look at him, as he sat on the rug and looked up at me, and think: "Oh, that dog will never live. He will be snatched up to the bright skies in a chariot, that is what will happen to him."

But, when I had paid for about a dozen chickens that he had killed; and had dragged him, growling and kicking, by the scruff of his neck, out of a hundred and fourteen street fights; and I had had a dead cat brought round for my inspection by an angry female, who called me a murderer; and had been taken to court by the man next-door-but-one for having a wild dog at large, that had kept him pinned up in his own tool-shed, afraid to come out for over two hours on a cold night; and had learned that the gardener, unknown to myself, had won quite a lot of money by backing the dog to kill rats in a certain length of time, then I began to think that maybe they'd let him remain on earth for a bit longer, after all.

To hang about a stable, and collect a gang of the scruffiest dogs to be found in the town, and to lead them out to march round the slums to fight other scruffy dogs, is Montmorency's idea of "life", and so he was quite keen on the idea of stopping at pubs with stables on our river holiday.

The wretched dog made his presence felt as soon as the three of us started packing for our holiday. He was in it all, of course. Montmorency's ambition in life is to get in the way and be sworn at. If he can squirm in anywhere where he is particularly not wanted, and be a perfect nuisance, and make people mad, and have things thrown at his head, then he feels that his day has not been wasted.

To get somebody to stumble over him, and curse him steadily for an hour, is his highest aim and object; and, when he has succeeded in this, his conceit becomes quite unbearable.

He came and sat down on things, just when they were wanted to be packed; and he had the idea that whenever Harris or George reached out their hands for anything, it was his cold damp nose they wanted. He put his leg into the jam, and he worried the teaspoons, and he pretended that the lemons were rats, and got into the hamper and killed three of them before Harris could hit him with the frying pan.

Harris said I encouraged him. I didn't encourage him. A dog like that doesn't want any encouragement. It's the natural sin that is born in him that makes him do things like that.

When we actually got going on the holiday Montmorency was no better. He let us down very badly on the first day. We had moored the boat at Marlow and decided to go for a walk along the High Street there. Coming along the road we met a cat.

When Montmorency meets a cat, the whole street knows about it; and there is enough bad language wasted in ten seconds to last an ordinary respectable man all his life, with care.

Half-way along the High Street a cat darted out from one of the houses in front of us, and began to trot across the road. Montmorency gave a cry of joy and flew after his prey.

His victim was a large black tom. I never saw a larger cat, nor a tougher-looking one. It had lost half its tail, one of its ears, and a large portion of its nose. It was a long, strong-looking animal. It had a calm, contented look about it.

Montmorency went for that poor cat at a tremendous speed; but the cat did not hurry up—it did not seem to have grasped the idea that its life was in danger. It trotted quietly on until the terrier was almost upon it, and then it turned round and sat in the middle of the road, and looked at Montmorency with a gentle, inquiring expression that said:

"Yes! You want me?"

Montmorency does not lack courage; but there was something about the look of that cat that might have chilled the heart of the boldest dog. He stopped abruptly, and looked at the tom.

Neither spoke, but the conversation that one could imagine was clearly as follows:

THE CAT: "Can I do anything for you?"

MONTMORENCY: "No—no, thanks."

THE CAT: "Don't mind speaking, if you really want anything, you know."

MONTMORENCY: (*backing down the High Street*): "Oh no—not at all—certainly—don't you trouble. I—I am afraid I've made a mistake. I thought I knew you. Sorry I disturbed you."

THE CAT: "Not at all—quite a pleasure. Sure you don't want anything, now?"

MONTMORENCY: (*still backing*): "Not at all, thanks—not at all—very kind of you. Good morning."

THE CAT: "Good morning."

Then the cat rose, and continued his trot; and Montmorency, fitting what he calls his tail carefully into its groove, came back to us, and took up an unimportant position in the rear.

To this day, if you say the word "Cats!" to Montmorency, he will visibly shrink and look up piteously at you, as if to say: "Please don't."

Neither was the dog a great help when it came to helping with the cooking. One evening George offered to cook us a magnificent stew on the banks of the river. It seemed a great idea. George gathered wood and lit a fire, and we threw plenty of potatoes into the pot, and half a pork pie, and a few cracked eggs, and a bit of cold boiled bacon, and half a tin of potted salmon.

I forget what else we added, but I know nothing was wasted. Towards the end, Montmorency, who had shown great interest in the proceedings throughout, strolled away with an earnest and thoughtful air. He reappeared a few minutes afterwards, with a dead water-rat in his mouth, which he evidently wished to present as his contribution to the dinner; whether in a sarcastic spirit, or with a general desire to assist, I cannot say.

It was a great success, that Irish stew. We finished up with tea and cherry tart. Montmorency had a fight with the kettle during tea-time, and came off a poor second.

Throughout the trip he had seemed puzzled by the kettle. He would sit and watch it as it boiled, with a blank expression. He would try to rouse it every now and then by growling at it. When it began to splutter and steam he regarded it as a challenge, and would want to fight it, only, at that precise moment, someone would always dash up and bear the kettle away before he could get at it.

Today he made up his mind to succeed. At the first sound the kettle made, he rose, growling, and advanced towards it. It was only a little kettle, but it was full of courage, and it up and spat at him.

"Ah! would you!" growled Montmorency, showing his teeth; "I'll teach you to cheek a hard-working, respectable dog; you miserable, long-nosed, dirty-looking scoundrel, you. Come on!"

And he rushed at that poor little kettle, and seized it by the spout.

Then, across the evening stillness, broke a blood-curdling yelp, and Montmorency left the boat, and ran three times round the island, stopping every now and then to bury his nose in a bit of cool mud.

From that day Montmorency regarded the kettle with a mixture of awe, suspicion and hate. Whenever he saw it, he would growl and back at a rapid rate, with his tail shut down, and the moment it was put up on the stove he would promptly climb out of the boat, and sit on the bank, till the whole tea business was over.

George got out his banjo after supper, and wanted to play it. He met with little success. Harris's language was enough to put any man off; added to which, Montmorency sat and howled steadily, right through the performance. It was not giving a man a fair chance.

"What does he want to howl like that for when I'm playing?" George exclaimed indignantly, while taking aim at the dog with a boot.

"What do you want to play like that for when he is howling?" Harris retorted, catching the boot. "You let him alone. He can't help howling. He's got a musical ear, and your playing *makes* him howl."

So George gave up the study of the banjo until he got home.

Of all the towns we visited as we sailed up the Thames, Montmorency preferred Oxford. We spent two very pleasant days there. There are plenty of dogs in the town of Oxford. Montmorency had eleven fights on the first day, and fourteen on the second, and evidently thought that he had gone to heaven.

Even when Montmorency was quiet I did not altogether trust him. He is a fox-terrier, and fox-terriers are born with about four times as much sin in them as other dogs.

I remember being in the lobby of the Haymarket Stores one day, and all round about me were dogs, waiting for the return of their owners who were shopping inside. There was a mastiff, and one or two collies, and a St Bernard, a few retrievers and Newfoundlands, a boar-hound, a French poodle, with plenty of hair round its head, but mangy in the middle; a bulldog, and a couple of Yorkshire tykes.

There they sat, patient, good, and thoughtful. Peace seemed to reign in the lobby. Then a sweet young lady entered, leading a meek-looking fox-terrier, and left him, chained up there, between the bulldog and the poodle. He sat and looked about him for a minute. Then he cast his eyes up to the ceiling, and seemed, judging from his expression, to be thinking of his mother. Then he yawned. Then he looked round at the other dogs, all silent; grave and good.

He looked at the bulldog, sleeping dreamlessly on his right. He looked at the poodle, straight and proud, on his left. Then, without a word of warning, he bit the poodle on the leg. A yelp of agony rang through the quiet shades of the lobby.

The fox-terrier obviously then decided to make things lively all round. He sprang over the poodle and attacked a collie, and the collie woke up and at once started a noisy battle with the poodle. The fox-terrier came back to his own place, and caught the bulldog by his ear, and tried to throw him away. The bulldog went for everything he could reach, including the hall-porter. This gave the dear little fox-terrier the chance to enjoy a fight of his own with an equally willing Yorkshire tyke.

By this time all the other dogs in the place were fighting as if their lives depended upon it.

The whole lobby seemed upside down, and the din was terrific.
A crowd gathered outside the store, asking who was being
murdered, and why? Men came with poles and ropes, and tried to
separate the dogs, and the police were sent for.

In the midst of the riot that sweet young lady returned, and
snatched up that sweet little dog of hers (he had laid the tyke up for
a month, and had on the expression, now, of a new-born lamb) into
her arms, and kissed him, and asked if he was killed, and what
those great nasty brutes of dogs had been doing to him; and he
gazed up into her face with a look that seemed to say: "Oh, I'm so
glad you've come to take me away from this disgraceful scene!"

She said that the people at the store had no right to allow great
savage things like those other dogs to be put with respectable
people's dogs, and that she had a great mind to report them to
somebody.

Such is the nature of fox-terriers, and, therefore, knowing him as I do, I always regard Montmorency with great caution. However, I must admit that on that trip there was one occasion when the sound of his bark was the sweetest noise I had ever heard.

It happened one night. We had moored the boat among many others among a group of islands in the river. George and I left Harris and Montmorency on board and went ashore to walk round Henley. We agreed that when we returned, we would shout from the shore and that Harris would row ashore in the small boat and collect us.

"Don't go asleep, old man," we warned him as we left.

The town of Henley was full of bustle that night. We met a fair number of people we knew about the town, and in their pleasant company the time slipped by somewhat quickly. It was nearly eleven o'clock before we left to walk back to our boat.

It was a dismal night, coldish, with a thin rain falling; and as we trudged through the dark, silent fields, talking low to each other, and wondering if we were going in the right direction, we thought of the cosy boat, with the bright light streaming through the tight-drawn canvas; of Harris and Montmorency waiting for us, and wished that we were there.

We struck the tow-path running along the river bank at length. We passed Shiplake as the clock was striking the quarter to twelve; and then George said thoughtfully:

"You don't happen to remember which of the islands it was, do you?"

"No," I replied, beginning to grow thoughtful too. "I don't. How many are there?"

"Only four," answered George. "It will be all right, if Harris is awake."

"And if not?" I asked, but we dismissed that thought.

We shouted when we came opposite the first island, but there was no reply; so we went on to the second and tried there, and got the same result.

"Oh! I remember now," said George, "it was the third one."

And we ran on hopefully to the third island, and shouted.

No answer!

The case was becoming serious. It was now past midnight. The hotels at Henley would be crammed; and we could not go round, knocking at doors in the middle of the night, asking for a bed.

In despair we tried the fourth island, but met with no better success. The rain was coming down fast now. We were wet to the skin, and cold and miserable. We began to wonder whether there were four islands or more, or whether, in the dark, we were even near any islands.

Just as we had given up all hope, I thought I caught sight of a flicker of a light out on the water. I shouted loudly and waited. Then, to our joy, we heard the answering bark of Montmorency. The dog barked loud and long enough to wake up Harris, for in about five minutes we saw the lighted rowing boat coming towards us in the dark, and heard Harris's sleepy voice asking where we were.

Slowly he took us back to our boat. Oh, how delightful it was to be safe on board after all our trials and fears. We ate a hearty supper, George and I, and for the first time in ages we looked approvingly at Montmorency!

THE WAR HORSE

from "Black Beauty" – by Anna Sewell

Sometimes in my dreams I hear the noise of battle again. The cannons roar in my ears. The shouts of the dead and dying echo through the night.

Captain is my name. I am a war-horse. It is my job to carry my master into battle.

When I was still a very young horse I was chosen by an army officer for this task. The year was about 1853. My officer served in the cavalry. Cavalry soldiers charge at the enemy on horseback, their swords in their hands.

After it was decided that I had the makings of a war-horse I had to be trained for the job. At first I found this very pleasant. There were many horses all together. We were well fed and well looked after.

We did our training in a large field next to an army camp. There were at least fifty of us. Every morning we turned out, looking very smart, with our masters on our backs.

For weeks we were trained to trot together in straight lines. At the word of command we would turn to the left or to the right. If a trumpet sounded over the field we would all dash forwards at great speed. I found this part very exciting.

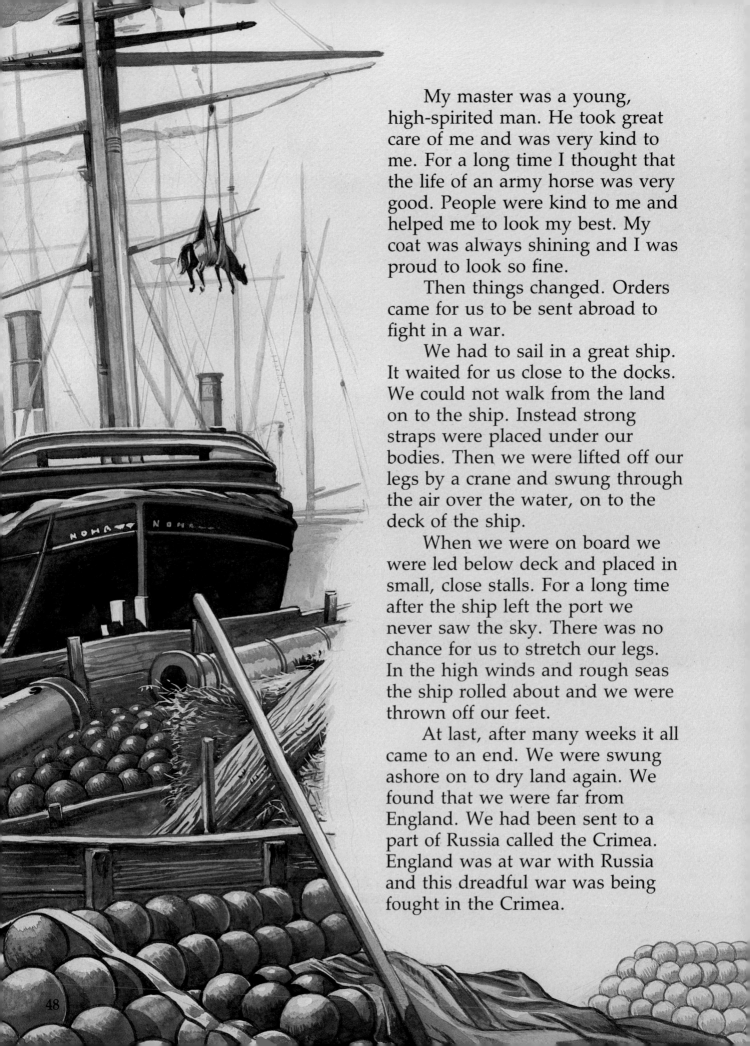

My master was a young, high-spirited man. He took great care of me and was very kind to me. For a long time I thought that the life of an army horse was very good. People were kind to me and helped me to look my best. My coat was always shining and I was proud to look so fine.

Then things changed. Orders came for us to be sent abroad to fight in a war.

We had to sail in a great ship. It waited for us close to the docks. We could not walk from the land on to the ship. Instead strong straps were placed under our bodies. Then we were lifted off our legs by a crane and swung through the air over the water, on to the deck of the ship.

When we were on board we were led below deck and placed in small, close stalls. For a long time after the ship left the port we never saw the sky. There was no chance for us to stretch our legs. In the high winds and rough seas the ship rolled about and we were thrown off our feet.

At last, after many weeks it all came to an end. We were swung ashore on to dry land again. We found that we were far from England. We had been sent to a part of Russia called the Crimea. England was at war with Russia and this dreadful war was being fought in the Crimea.

The land in which we had arrived was very different to
England. Life was hard there. We lived in great camps which held
many tents. Our masters did their best to look after us. Most of
them were very fond of their horses. They did everything that they
could to help us, in spite of the cold, the rain and the snow.

It was not long before we were sent into battle. We took part in a number of engagements. Sometimes we had to stand waiting for hours before the order to move was given. But then the trumpet would sound and we would advance. That was the part I always liked best.

When the order to charge was given we would leap forward at a great rate. We paid no heed to the cannon balls, bullets and bayonets that awaited us at the end of the charge. As long as we felt our rider firm and safe in the saddle, and his hand steady on the reins, not one of us was afraid.

My noble master and I were in many actions together without a wound. Around me I saw horses shot down with bullets, cut with lances, and gashed by swords. I never feared for myself. My master's cheery voice made me feel as if he and I could not be killed.

I saw many brave men cut down. I heard the cries and groans of the dying. I cantered over ground slippery with blood. But I never felt terror – until one dreadful day I shall never forget.

One autumn morning we turned out an hour before dawn, ready for work. The men stood by their horses, waiting for orders. The light grew brighter and in the distance we could hear the sound of guns.

One of the officers rode up and gave the order to mount. In a second every man was in his saddle. Every horse stood waiting. My dear master and I were at the head of the line.

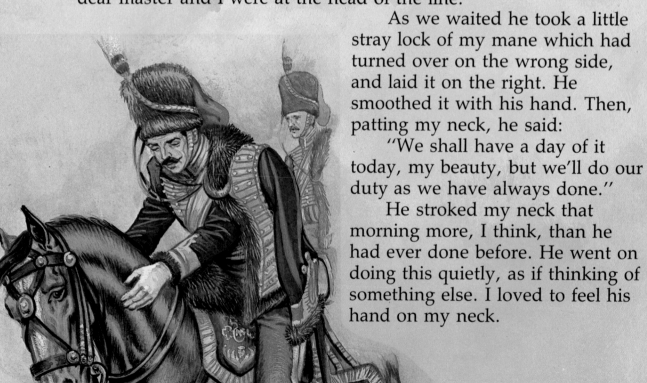

As we waited he took a little stray lock of my mane which had turned over on the wrong side, and laid it on the right. He smoothed it with his hand. Then, patting my neck, he said:

"We shall have a day of it today, my beauty, but we'll do our duty as we have always done."

He stroked my neck that morning more, I think, than he had ever done before. He went on doing this quietly, as if thinking of something else. I loved to feel his hand on my neck.

I cannot tell all that happened that day, but I will tell of the last
charge we made. We rode across a valley right in front of the
enemy's guns. By this time we were well used to their roar, the
rattle of musket fire, and the flying of shot near us. But never had I
been under such fire as we rode through on that day.

From the right, from the left, and from the front, shot and shell
poured in on us. Many a brave man went down. Many a horse fell,
flinging his rider to the earth. Many a horse without a rider ran
wildly out of the ranks.

Fearful as it was, no one stopped, no one turned back. Every
moment the ranks of the riders were thinned. As our comrades fell
we closed in closer together. We drew closer to the cannon, all
clouded in white smoke, with the red fire flashing through it. Our
pace became faster and faster.

My master, my dear master, was cheering on his comrades with his right arm raised on high. One of the great iron balls struck him. I felt him stagger with the shock, though he made no sound. I tried to check my speed, but the sword dropped from his right hand, the rein fell from his left, and he fell to the earth.

The other riders swept past us. By the force of their charge I was driven from the spot where he fell.

I wanted to keep my place by his side, and not leave him under the rush of horses' feet, but it was in vain. Now, without a master or friend, I was alone on that great killing ground. Fear took me as it had never taken me before.

I trembled and tried to join the ranks of the horses still with riders. Men beat me off with the flats of their swords, in case I got in their way and brought them down.

Just then, a soldier whose horse had been killed under him, caught at my bridle and mounted me. With this new master I again went forward. But our brave company could go no further. The ground was thick with bodies. Still the guns fired. Those who remained alive after the fierce battle for guns, came riding back over the same ground.

Some of the horses were so badly wounded that they could hardly move for loss of blood. Others were trying to drag themselves along on three legs. A few tried to drag themselves to their feet. Their groans were awful to hear. The battle was over.

Afterwards soldiers went out with guns to shoot the badly wounded horses. The ones which were not so badly hurt were brought back and helped. In our stables only one in four were left alive.

I never saw my dear master again. I believe he fell dead from the saddle. I never loved another master so well. I went into other battles, but was only once wounded. When the war was over I returned to England, as sound and strong as when I went out.

Sometimes I wonder what the war was all about. Why did my fine young master have to die? But it is all too much for me. To tell the truth, I can think of no reason for it at all.

COYOTE, OR THE PRAIRIE WOLF

by Francis Bret Harte

Blown out of the prairie in twilight and dew,
Half bold and half timid, yet lazy all through;
Loth ever to leave, and yet fearful to stay,
He limps in the clearing, – an outcast in grey.

A shade on the stubble, a ghost by the wall,
Now leaping, now limping, now risking a fall,
Lop-eared and large-jointed, but ever alway
A thoroughly vagabond outcast in grey.

Here, Carlo, old fellow, he's one of your kind, –
Go seek him, and bring him in out of the wind.
What! snarling, my Carlo! So – even dogs may
Deny their own kin in the outcast in grey!

Well, take what you will, – though it be on the sly,
Marauding or begging, – I shall not ask why;
But will call it a dole, just to help on his way
A four-footed friar in orders of grey!

THE PICK OF THE PUPPIES

from "Jock of the Bushveld"
by Sir Percy Fitzpatrick

I needed a dog. My job in South Africa many years ago was to bring food and supplies up to the gold mining camps in waggons, drawn by teams of oxen. A number of waggons would travel together in this way on long, hard journeys for many days at a time, resting at night.

I felt that a good dog would serve both as a friend and as a guard. Finding one, however, was no easy task.

One day, old Jess, a bull-terrier belonging to Ted, one of the other transport riders, gave birth to six puppies. Ted said that he was willing to get rid of them.

The puppies were kept with their mother in a nest in one of the waggons. Five of the pups were fat, strong, yellow little chaps with dark muzzles. The sixth was different. He was a poor little rat of a thing, about half the size of the others. He was not yellow like them, but a sort of dirty pale half-and-half colour with some dark, faint wavy lines all over him.

Most of the fellows said it would be a good thing to drown the odd one because he spoiled the litter. But in the end he was allowed to live.

I offered to take him rather than let him be drowned. All the other puppies had already been claimed by drivers who knew Ted better than I did. Ted agreed that I might take the puppy when he was ready to leave his mother.

As they grew older and were able to crawl about, the pups were taken off the waggons when we camped for the night and put on the ground. Jess would watch us quietly as we took them in our hands, to put them down or lift them back again.

I began to look after the sixth puppy. I felt sorry for him because he was small and weak. The other puppies used to push him away from his food and trample on him. When they were old enough to play they used to pull his ears and bully him. Many a time I had to rescue him and feed him on bread and milk.

I began to notice little things about him. I got to be quite fond of the little beggar. He was always cheerful and brave and it seemed that there might be some good stuff in him after all.

The other puppies would tumble over him and take his food from him. They would bump into him when he was stooping over the dish of milk and porridge. His head was so big and his legs so weak that he would tip up and go head over heels into the dish. We were always picking him out of the food and scraping it off him. Half the time he was wet and sticky, and the other half covered with porridge and sand, baked hard by the sun.

One day just after the waggons had started, I took a final look round to see if anything had been left behind. I found the little chap – who was still tiny – trying to walk through the long grass. He was not big enough or strong enough to push his way through. He stumbled and tripped at every step, but he got up again each time with his little tail standing straight up, his head erect, and his ears cocked.

He looked as proud and important as if he owned the whole world. How he fell out of the waggon no one knew. Perhaps the big puppies had pushed him out.

The other transport riders thought more of the sixth puppy when I caught up with them and told them of his brave efforts to walk through the long grass. But they continued to call him 'The Rat'. He really was very ugly, and as he grew older he got worse.

He was very silent, hardly ever barking. One day however he did make a noise. One of the oxen caught sight of the pup all alone and came up to sniff at him. 'The Rat' stood quite still with his stumpy tail cocked up and his head a little on one side. When the huge ox's nose was just in front of him he gave a funny, sharp little bark. It was as if he had exploded like a firecracker. The ox nearly fell over with fright and turned and trotted off.

'The Rat' was not a bit like other puppies. If anyone fired off a gun or cracked one of the big whips the whole five would yell at the top of their voices and would run away at once. The odd puppy would drop his bone with a start, or would jump round. His ears and tail would flicker up and down for a second. Then he would slowly bristle all over, and with his head cocked first on one side and then on the other, stare hard towards the noise. But he never ran away.

No matter how many of the other puppies attacked him, or how they bit or pulled him, he never once let out a yelp. With four or five on top of him you would see him on his back, snapping left and right with his bare white teeth.

Before long it was plain that most of the other puppies were leaving 'The Rat' alone. The reason was obvious. Instead of wasting his breath in making a noise, the odd puppy simply bit hard and hung on. No one could bully him, he fought back too hard.

The day came when Ted announced to the rest of us that the puppies were now ready to leave their mother. We could come along to his waggon and collect them.

As the drivers gathered before the waggon Ted came out.

"Bill can't take his pup," he told us.

Every man among us stepped forward. Bill's pup was the first pick, the best of the litter, the biggest and strongest of the lot. Several of the others said that they would take it. Ted shook his head.

"No," he said, "you had a good pick in the first place." Then he turned to me and said: "You only had the last choice. You can have Bill's pup if you like."

It seemed too good to be true. I could hardly wait to pick up the best pup. I went forward to claim him from the pile. As I did so the odd puppy came forward and licked my hand.

I had forgotten all about him. But the sight of him made me think of his odd ways, his bravery, and the fact that I was the only friend he had in the world. I knew what I must do.

"Ted," I said, waiting to hear the others laugh. "If you don't mind, I'll stick to 'The Rat'."

If I had fired off a gun the others could not have been more surprised. When they saw that I meant what I said, Ted spoke for all of them.

"Well, I'm hanged," he said.

"He's mine," I said firmly.

I took him in hand at once – for now he really belonged to me – and set about training the pup. Dogs are like people. What they learn when they are young they do not forget. I began early with 'The Rat', and tried to help him.

To start with I gave him a new name. From now on he was Jock, and that was how he was known to everyone.

Then I began to teach him obedience. The lesson began when he got his saucer of porridge in the morning. I put it in front of him and then tapped him on the nose each time he tried to dive into it.

At first he fought to get at it. Then he tried to back away and dodge round the other side. Then he became dazed, and thought it was not meant for him at all.

In a few days, however, I got him to lie still and take the food only when I patted him and pushed him towards it. In a very little time he got on so well that I could put his food down and he would not touch it until I told him to.

Jock would lie with his head on his paws and his nose right up against the saucer, so as to lose no time when the order came. But he would not touch it until the order came: "Take it".

His courage became well known among the miners and transport drivers. One day, while he was still a puppy, he finished his saucer of food under the rough camp table on which we put our food to keep it from the ants.

He had been standing close to the leg of the table. He stretched lazily and his hip came into contact with the table leg.

In an instant he changed completely. The hair on his back bristled. His head went up at one end and his tail at the other. He shook with rage. He thought that one of the other pups had come up on him from behind.

He was too proud to look round and appear nervous. He glared straight ahead and growled. He stood like that, not moving. Then he relaxed and stretched again.

The same thing happened again. His hip struck the table; he thought he was being stalked, and he growled with rage. One could not imagine so small a dog being in so great a temper.

Again, after a long time, he relaxed. Again his hip touched the table leg. This time it was all over in a second. Jock seemed to feel that three times was more than any dog could stand. He turned round with a great snarl – and bumped his nose against the table leg.

A great shout of laughter went up from all the men. Jock looked rather foolish. He gave us a feeble wag of his tail and waddled off as fast as he could.

Then Ted nodded over at me, and said: "I believe you have got the best after all!"

And I was too proud to speak.

61

THE CHASE

from "Moby Dick" – by Herman Melville

For years Captain Ahab had chased the great white whale, known as Moby Dick, from sea to sea. He swore that one day he would find the beast and destroy it.

Ahab hated the white whale with a great passion that filled his life. Once he had sailed his ship close to the monster, but Moby Dick had been too quick and too strong. He had turned on the whalers and put them to flight. In doing so he had delivered a terrible blow on Ahab, shattering his leg and causing him to lose it.

Somehow he got back to port, fitted out another vessel and gathered a crew to go in search of the white whale.

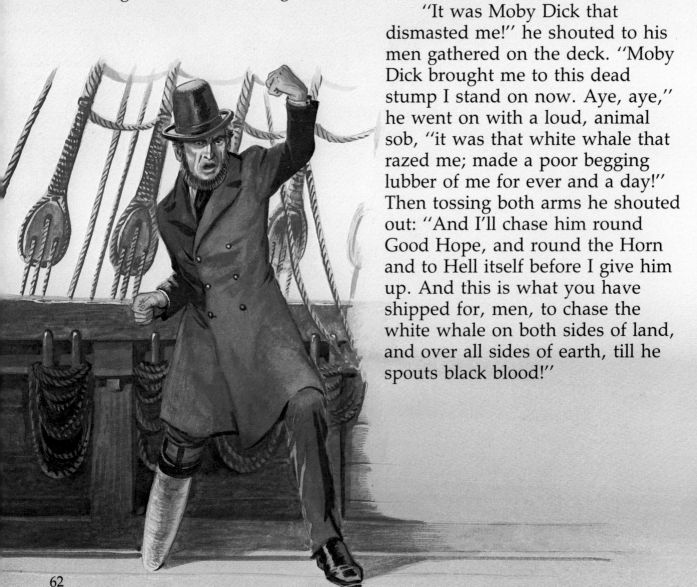

"It was Moby Dick that dismasted me!" he shouted to his men gathered on the deck. "Moby Dick brought me to this dead stump I stand on now. Aye, aye," he went on with a loud, animal sob, "it was that white whale that razed me; made a poor begging lubber of me for ever and a day!" Then tossing both arms he shouted out: "And I'll chase him round Good Hope, and round the Horn and to Hell itself before I give him up. And this is what you have shipped for, men, to chase the white whale on both sides of land, and over all sides of earth, till he spouts black blood!"

So the great voyage began. From sea to sea the whaling ship *Pequod* sailed in search of Moby Dick. Month after month passed and the whale was not seen. Then one day, in the Great South Sea, Captain Ahab came up on to the deck at first light.

"What do you see?" he called to the look-outs.

"Nothing, sir!" came back from the men perched at the tops of the masts.

The captain tied about him the life-line which was used to haul him up to the main mast-head. In a moment he was on his way up to the top. When he was about two-thirds of the way up he peered into the distance, and suddenly raised a gull-like cry into the air, "There she blows! There she blows! A hump like a snow-hill! It is Moby Dick!"

His cry was taken up by the three look-outs. The men on deck rushed to the rigging to behold the famous whale they had so long been hunting. Ahab reached his final perch, some way below the other look-outs. From this height the whale was now seen some mile or so ahead. Every roll of the sea revealed his high sparkling hump, and the jet of water spouting high into the air.

"There she blows!" cried Ahab again. "Stand by to lower three boats. Keep her steady! Bring me down to the deck again! Quickly, quickly!"

"He's heading right away from us," shouted a look-out. "He cannot have seen the ship yet."

"Boats!" screamed Ahab. "Lower the boats!"

Soon the three boats had been lowered into the water and were being rowed in the direction of the unsuspecting white whale. Ahab sat quivering in the prow of the leading boat.

Like hollow shells the light craft sped through the sea, but only slowly neared the whale. The ocean grew more smooth, as if a carpet were being spread over the waves.

Before long, the white whale was clearly visible, his hump sliding along the sea, set in a revolving ring of green foam. Slowly the fore part of the great beast rose out of the water, forming a large arch, like some enormous bridge. It hung there for a moment, and then the white whale dived and was gone from view.

"We'll wait an hour," gritted Ahab.

"The birds! – the birds!" cried one of the rowers.

A long line of white sea-birds seemed to be flying directly to the boat containing Ahab. Their sight was keener than that of the sailors'. As Ahab peered down into the water he saw a white spot, no bigger than a weasel. Then two long crooked rows of white teeth began to float up from the bottom.

It was Moby Dick's open mouth, his vast bulk still half-blending with the blue of the sea. The glittering mouth yawned beneath the boat. Giving one sweep with his steering oar Ahab whirred the craft aside. Then he called to one of the seamen to take his place in the prow. Picking up a harpoon, the captain poised himself to strike when the whale appeared.

By spinning the boat Ahab had hoped to avoid the whale as it surfaced. But Moby Dick was as quick and as intelligent as any man, and much stronger. The great whale changed direction while still coming up, and placed itself beneath the craft again.

It came up just in front of the prow, its mouth open like a gigantic shark. Slowly the whale took the bow of the boat in its mouth and began to shake it.

The seamen left their oars and fled to the stern. A second later Moby Dick had bitten the boat completely in half! Ahab and the others were spilled out into the sea.

Moby Dick swam swiftly round and round the wrecked crew, churning the water in his wake, as if lashing himself up to still another and more deadly assault. The sight of the splintered boat seemed to madden him, and the sailors clinging to the wreckage wondered if their end had come.

The men remaining on board *Pequod* had seen what was happening from the ship's mast-heads. Swiftly they sailed the whaler towards the struggling sailors.

"Sail on the whale!" shouted Captain Ahab. "Drive him off!"

The *Pequod's* prows were pointed, and the vessel headed for the white whale. Reluctantly Moby Dick turned and swam off. As he did so, the boats flew to the rescue.

Ahab was dragged over the side of one of the craft. He pulled himself upright, demanding: "The harpoon – is it safe?"

"Aye, sir!"

"Any missing men?"

"One, two, three, four, five; – there were five oars, sir, and here are five men."

"That's good. Which way is the whale swimming?"

Moby Dick was now making good speed. The only hope of catching up with the whale lay in the *Pequod*. The two boats and the remains of the third were hauled on board. Hoisting every inch of sail, the *Pequod* bore down after Moby Dick.

"There she blows!" came a cry from the mast-head.

The thirty men on board the *Pequod* worked as one, just as the ship which carried them was one vessel although made of many different things – oak and maple, and pine wood; iron, and pitch, and hemp. All these things ran into each other in the one solid hull, which shot on its way like a cannon-ball.

The rigging lived. The mast-heads, like the tops of tall palms, were tufted with arms and legs. Clinging to a spar with one hand, some reached forth the other with impatient wavings; others, shading their eyes from the vivid sunlight, sat far out on the rocking sails. Ah, how they tried to seek out the thing that might destroy them!

"Lower the boats!" ordered Ahab at last.

Once more the ship's boats were swung out and lowered into the sea. Captain Ahab was about to descend into the leading one, when he turned to Starbuck, the mate.

"I am old," he said. "Shake hands with me, man."

Their hands and eyes met. "Oh, my captain, my captain, do not go," begged the mate.

"Lower away!" cried Ahab, tossing the mate's arm from him. "Stand by, the crew!"

In an instant the boat was pulling round close under the stern. Numbers of sharks rose out of the dark waters beneath the hull, snapping at the blades of the oars, every time they dipped into the water. The men strained their eyes. Moby Dick had dived beneath the surface again.

Suddenly the waters around them slowly swelled in broad circles. A low rumbling sound was heard and then a vast form shot out of the sea. The waters flashed like heaps of fountains, then sank in a shower of flakes.

"Give way!" cried Ahab to the oarsmen, and the boats darted forward to the attack. Moby Dick came forward in his turn, churning his tail among the boats; and once more flailed them apart. He spilled out the harpoons and lances from the two mates' boats, and dashed in one side of the upper part of their bows, but left Ahab's almost without a scar.

"Head for the whale!" cried Ahab again.

The seamen rowed their craft alongside the flank of Moby Dick. Soon they were within the smoky mountain mist thrown off from the whale's spout. Ahab balanced himself and hurled his lance into the beast's side, cursing fiercely.

Moby Dick crashed against the boat, writhing in agony. Ahab clutched the side, but three of the oarsmen were dashed into the water. Two managed to clamber back in, but the third was swept away.

For a moment it seemed as if the white whale would crush the small boat, but then Moby Dick caught a glimpse of the much larger *Pequod* and headed for that instead. He bore down on it, smiting his jaws amid fiery showers of foam.

From the ship's bows, nearly all the seamen hung, watching the approaching whale. Then the solid white wall of its forehead smote the ship's starboard bow. Men and timbers reeled. Some fell flat on their faces. The side of the ship splintered and water poured in.

Diving beneath the sinking ship, the whale ran quivering along its keel. It turned under the water and swiftly came to the surface again, and lay within a few yards of Ahab's boat.

Captain Ahab poised himself and flung yet another harpoon with deadly power at the beast.

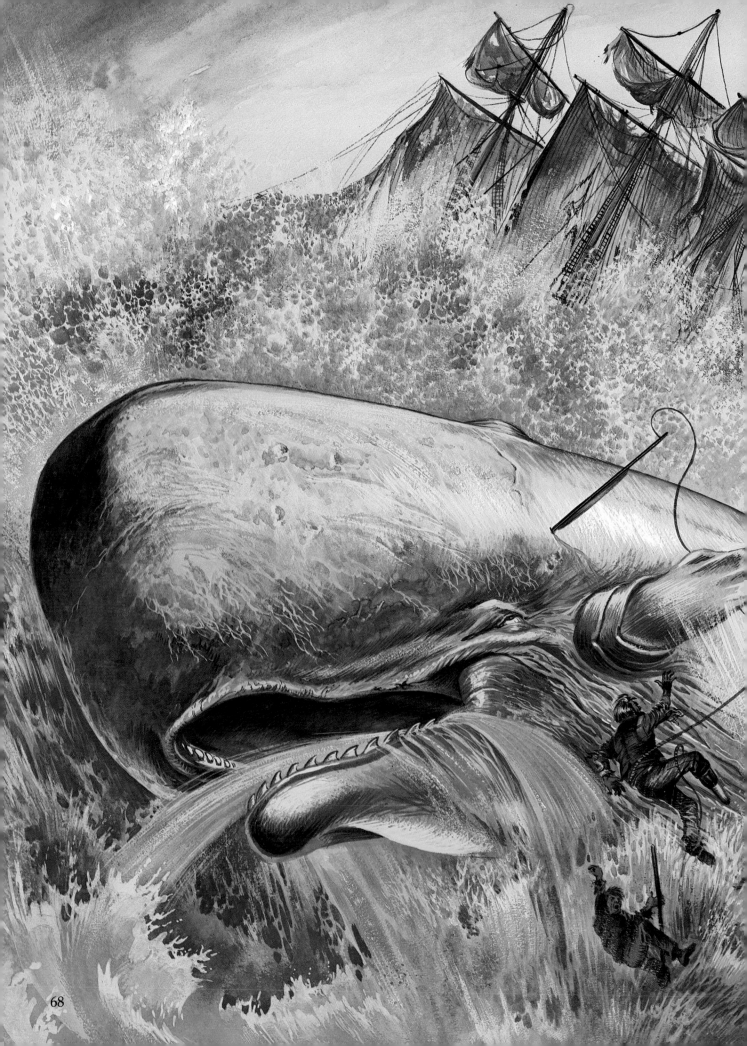

The lance flew out, taking
with it a long line. Moby Dick
shuddered as the harpoon sank
deeply into its body, killing it. In
its death-throes the beast gave one
last heave. The force of its pull
took Captain Ahab over the side,
to join the great white whale in
death.

"The ship! Look at the ship!"
screamed one of the remaining
oarsmen.

The seamen turned and gazed
across the sea. Only the
uppermost masts of the *Pequod*
were visible above the water. As
they watched in horror, even these
vanished beneath the waves.

IT WAS DREADFUL IN THE FOREST

from "The Lost World"
by Sir Arthur Conan Doyle

When I tell men that for a time I lived in a world of great prehistoric monsters, they do not believe me. And when I say that one of these beasts chased and hunted me down, they think I am mad.

But it is true, every word of it. It happened only a few years ago. My companions and I stumbled across this amazing lost world. It was as if time there had stood still. Nothing had changed since the dawn of time.

Great winged creatures swooped from the sky. Dinosaurs as big as houses roamed over the land, crushing trees beneath the weight of their feet. The plains and forests of this strange world were full of other huge beasts which men thought had died out thousands of years ago.

We found this fantastic world, my friends and I, in South America. It was thousands of miles up the great Amazon river, where no white men had ventured before.

I was the youngest of a small party of explorers. Over those amazing months we shared many dangers and adventures. Perhaps the most hair-raising was one encounter I had on my own.

We had made camp for the night in a large, dense forest. I could not sleep, and being young was not satisfied to lie staring up at the branches above me. I decided to explore a little on my own. I crept away from my companions as they snored in their sleeping bags next to the fire.

I had not gone more than a hundred metres before I was sorry. It was lonely in that great forest, and I did not know what lay before me. But I did not care to go back. Suppose one of my friends woke up and saw me? I would seem a fool for going out and a coward for coming back.

I pressed on with faltering footsteps. It was dreadful in the forest. The towering trees grew so thickly and their leaves and branches spread so widely that for long periods I could not see the moon above. Then suddenly it would shine through a gap and bathe the ground in a silvery light. Nervously I cradled my rifle in my arms and picked my way over the roots and mounds on the floor of the forest.

For a long time I saw no sign of any living thing, although I could hear many signs of them somewhere out in the darkness. After a while I came across a stream and began to follow its course. This in turn led me across a swamp. Here I came across the first of the great creatures I was to meet to my cost that night.

A great beast with wings, looking for all the world like a flying skeleton, rose up before me and soared through the air. I froze where I was, not daring to move. The creature flew into the trees and then returned and settled with a great beating of wings, sinking into its resting place in the swamp.

My heart was beating fast with the shock of this unexpected meeting, but I forced myself to move on. The night was growing still as the occupants of the forest settled to their rest. As I advanced, however, I became aware of a low, rumbling sound. This grew louder as I went on. Soon it was quite close to me. It was like a boiling kettle or the bubbling from some great pot.

Soon I came across its source. In the centre of a small clearing I found a lake of some black, pitch-like stuff. Its surface rose and fell in great blisters of bursting gas. The ground round about was so hot I could hardly bear to place my hand on it.

I had seen similar pools on my travels. Usually they were to be found on the slopes of craters. The horrible thought came to me that in addition to the rest of our perils we might be climbing the slopes of a volcano on our voyage of discovery. Were this to be true, and should the volcano explode there would be no hope for us.

I decided to hurry back to the camp and inform my companions of my find. It was a fearsome walk, and one which will be with me as long as my memory holds. In the great moonlit clearings I slunk along among the shadows on the edge. In the forest I crept forward, stopping with a beating heart if I heard, as I often did, the crash of breaking branches as some wild beast went past.

Now and then great shadows loomed up for an instant and were gone – great silent shadows which seemed to prowl upon padded feet. At last I saw the gleam of water amid the openings of the forest. Ten minutes later I was among the reeds upon the borders of the lake I had seen the day before.

I lay down and drank deeply. There was a broad path with many tracks upon it at the spot which I had found. It was clearly one of the drinking places of the animals. Close to the water's edge there was a huge flat rock. Up this I climbed and, lying on the top, I had an excellent view in every direction.

The lake lay like a sheet of quicksilver before me. The reflected moon shone brightly in the centre of it. It was shallow, for in many places I saw sandbanks poking above the water. On the still surface I could see signs of life. Upon a yellow sandbank I saw a creature like a huge swan, with a clumsy body and a high neck. Then it dived into the water, and I saw it no more.

Beneath me two creatures like enormous lizards had come down to the water to drink. They were squatting at the edge of the water, their long tongues like red ribbons shooting in and out as they lapped.

A huge deer with branching horns came down with its doe and two fawns. No such deer exists anywhere else on earth, for the biggest moose I have ever seen on earth would hardly have reached the shoulders of the one drinking at the lake.

Suddenly the great deer gave a warning snort and was off with its family among the reeds. The two great lizards also scuttled for shelter. A new-comer, a most monstrous animal, was coming down the path.

For a moment I wondered where I could have seen such an ungainly shape. The beast had an arched back, with triangular fringes along it, and a strange bird-like head held close to the ground. Behind it, dragging heavily over the ground, was an enormous tail. Great spikes of bone were attached to this tail, while slabs of bone covered the creature's body, almost like armour.

I wondered why I seemed to know such a fearful creature. Then it came to me. I had seen many drawings of the beast in books on dinosaurs, the creatures that walked the earth long before man appeared. This particular one was a stegosaurus.

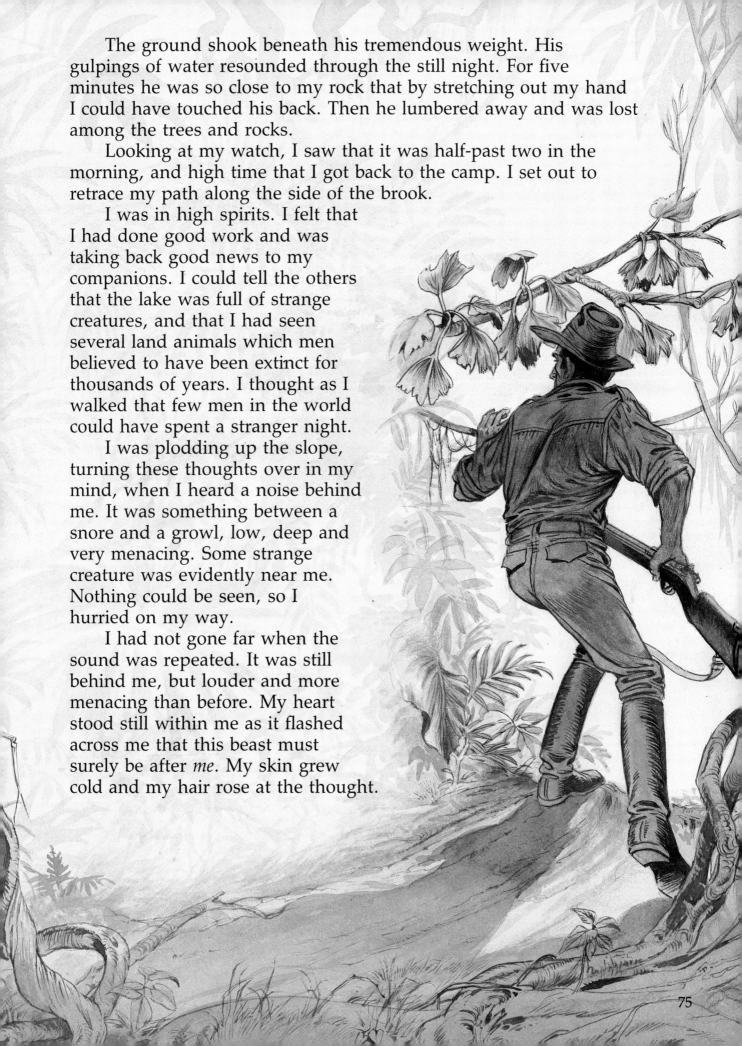

The ground shook beneath his tremendous weight. His gulpings of water resounded through the still night. For five minutes he was so close to my rock that by stretching out my hand I could have touched his back. Then he lumbered away and was lost among the trees and rocks.

Looking at my watch, I saw that it was half-past two in the morning, and high time that I got back to the camp. I set out to retrace my path along the side of the brook.

I was in high spirits. I felt that I had done good work and was taking back good news to my companions. I could tell the others that the lake was full of strange creatures, and that I had seen several land animals which men believed to have been extinct for thousands of years. I thought as I walked that few men in the world could have spent a stranger night.

I was plodding up the slope, turning these thoughts over in my mind, when I heard a noise behind me. It was something between a snore and a growl, low, deep and very menacing. Some strange creature was evidently near me. Nothing could be seen, so I hurried on my way.

I had not gone far when the sound was repeated. It was still behind me, but louder and more menacing than before. My heart stood still within me as it flashed across me that this beast must surely be after *me*. My skin grew cold and my hair rose at the thought.

With my knees shaking beneath me I stood and glared with staring eyes down the moonlit path which lay behind me. All was quiet as in a dream landscape. Silver clearings and the black patches of bushes – nothing else could I see. Then from out of the silence there came once more that low, throaty croaking, far louder and closer than before. There could no longer be a doubt. Something was on my trail, and it was closing in upon me every minute.

I stood still, staring back. Then I saw it. There was movement among the bushes near the far end of the clearing I had just come across. A great dark shadow appeared and hopped out into the clear moonlight.

I say 'hopped' for the beast moved like a kangaroo, springing along in an erect position on its powerful hind legs, while its front ones were held bent in front of it. It was of enormous size and power, like an erect elephant. In spite of its bulk its movements were quick and alert.

His ferocious cry and horrible energy both assured me that this was one of the great flesh-eating dinosaurs, the most terrible beasts which have ever walked the earth.

As the huge brute lopped along it dropped forward upon its forepaws and brought its nose to the ground every twenty metres or so. It was smelling out my trail. Sometimes, for an instant, it was at fault. Then it would catch up again and come bounding swiftly along the path I had taken.

Even now when I think of that nightmare the sweat breaks out upon my brow. What could I do? My useless rifle was in my hand. What help could I get from that. I looked round for some rock or tree, but I was in a bushy forest with nothing higher than a sapling in sight.

I knew that the creature behind me could tear down a tree as though it were a reed. My only possible chance lay in flight. I could not move swiftly over the rough, broken ground, but as I looked round me in despair I saw a well-marked, hard-beaten path which ran across in front of me. I had seen such paths before. They were the runs of wild beasts, worn down over the years.

Flinging away my gun, I set out to run faster than I had ever done before. My limbs ached, my chest heaved, I felt that my throat would burst for want of air. Yet with that horror behind me I ran and ran and ran.

At last I stopped, hardly able to move. For a moment I thought that I had thrown him off. The path lay still behind me. And then suddenly, with a crashing and a thudding of giant feet and a panting of monster lungs, the beast was upon me once more. He was at my very heels. I was lost.

Now he had actually seen me. I started running again. The beast came after me in great bounds. The moonlight shone upon his huge projecting eyes, the row of enormous teeth in his open mouth, and the gleaming fringe of claws upon his short powerful forearms.

With a scream of terror I turned and rushed wildly down the path. Behind me the thick, gasping breathing of the creature sounded louder and louder. His heavy footfall was beside me. Every instant I expected to feel his grip upon my back. And then suddenly there came a crash – I was falling through space, and everything beyond was darkness and rest.

When I came round I was aware of a most dreadful smell. Putting out my hand in the darkness, I came across something which felt like a huge lump of meat. Up above me there was a circle of starlit sky. I seemed to be lying at the bottom of a deep pit. Slowly I staggered to my feet and felt myself all over. I was stiff and sore from head to foot, but I did not seem to have broken anything.

Then I remembered what had caused my fall. I looked up in terror, expecting to see the dreadful head of the monster peering down at me. There was no sign of the beast, however, nor could I hear any sound from above. I began to feel my way around in an attempt to find out where I was.

I was in a pit with sharply sloping walls and a level bottom about seven metres across. This bottom was littered with great pieces of flesh. After tripping and stumbling over them, I came across something hard. I found that an upright post was firmly fixed in the centre of the hollow. It was so high that I could not reach the top of it with my hand. It appeared to be covered with grease.

I remembered that I had a box of matches in my pocket. I struck one of them. Then I realised where I was. I was in a trap, one made by the hand of man. The post in the centre was about three metres long. It was sharp at the upper end, and it was black with the stale blood of creatures who had been impaled upon it.

The remains scattered about the ground were fragments of the victims, which had been cut away in order to clear the stake for the next who might blunder in.

It was clear that there were people living in this lost world. In order to get meat they dug pits like this one, with great spears stuck in the bottom. They dug these pits across the paths made by animals, and covered the holes with branches and leaves, so that the beasts would fall into the pit, as I had. It was only by the mercy of God that I had missed the sharpened stake and fallen straight to the ground.

The sloping pit would not be difficult for me to climb, but how did I know that the dreadful creature was not waiting for me in the nearest clump of bushes? I remembered reading somewhere that the dinosaurs, although large of frame, had very small brains. They could not reason things out.

If this should be true, then the beast which had been chasing me would not have the intelligence to wait and see if I appeared again. It was a chance I had to take.

Slowly I climbed to the top of the pit. I poked my head up and looked round. The stars were fading, the sky was getting lighter, and the cold wind of morning blew pleasantly upon my face. I could see or hear nothing of my enemy.

Slowly I climbed out and sat for a while upon the ground, ready to spring back into the pit if any danger should appear. After a while I plucked up my courage and stole back along the path which I had come. Some way down it I picked up my gun. Soon afterwards I found the brook which was my guide. So, with many a frightened backward glance, I made for home.